SERGEI RACHMANINOFF
1873-1943

CÉSAR FRANCK
1822-1890

IGNACE PADEREWSKI
1860-1941

CHARLES WAKEFIELD CADMAN
1881-

ANTON RUBINSTEIN
1829-1894

HENRY K. HADLEY
1871-1937

ETHELBERT
NEVIN
1862-1901

EDITED BY

ALBERT E. WIER

Volume VI

Standard & Modern Dance Music

PIANO

CHARLES SCRIBNER'S SONS, NEW YORK

Printed in the United States of America

E-4. 63 (SQ)

THE SCRIBNER MUSIC LIBRARY

Volume VI—Standard and Modern Dance Music

TABLE OF CONTENTS—TITLES

THE SCRIBNER MUSIC LIBRARY

VOLUME VI—STANDARD AND MODERN DANCE MUSIC

TABLE OF CONTENTS—COMPOSERS

A Guide Through Volume VI

THE volumes of The SCRIBNER MUSIC LIBRARY are devoted entirely to compositions which are heard constantly over the great broadcasting chains—played by orchestras, chamber music organizations or instrumental soloists; sung by choral organizations or by vocal soloists. Each of the volumes contains only the choicest and most popular of its particular type of music.

This volume is devoted to the choicest standard dance compositions which could be selected out of the thousands that are played every year over the air—for dance music has inspired the creative instinct in composers of all countries, and themes as exquisite as those used in serious compositions are frequently to be found in them.

GERMAN COMPOSERS

Germany boasts quite justly of a long line of distinguished dance composers, and we have been able to select for this volume the works of several composers which are frequently broadcast. Josef Bayer has conceived a lovely and dainty set of **Doll Waltzes** founded on themes from his "Fairy Doll" ballet; a beautiful set of slow waltzes called **Sounds From Home** emanate from the pen of Josef Gung'l; Otto Roeder charms us with his **Love's Dreamland** Waltzes, and there is sensuous sway in Steck's **Flirtation** Waltzes. There is also much of imagination and melody in Spacek's **Night Frolic** and Steger's **Haven of Happiness,** both exquisite slow waltzes.

JOHANN STRAUSS, JR.

In the realm of waltzes, however, Vienna may claim that her favorite son, Johann Strauss, Jr., was and is still to-day the king of waltz composers—to say nothing of his distinguished father, Johann, Sr., and his brothers, Josef and Edward. In this volume it is chiefly with Johann, Jr., that we have to do, for there are no less than ten waltzes of his composition to be found in it. There is that masterpiece of masterpieces, **The Blue Danube,** the superb **Artist Life,** the cheery **Morning Journals,** the flashing **New Vienna,** the dainty **Roses from the South** (from melodies in his operetta, "The Queen's Lace Handkerchief"), the swaying **Treasure Waltz** from melodies in his operetta, "The Gipsy Baron"; then there is the fantastic **Tales from the Vienna Woods,** fairly breathing romance; the vivacious **Voices of Spring,** which has become a popular vocal waltz; the **Vienna Blood,** cleverly descriptive of the dandies in that gay city; and still another set of waltzes teeming with life and gayety, titled **Wine, Women and Song.** As a relief to all these waltz rhythms, you will also find his charming mazurka, **One Heart, One Mind,** and a brilliant composition in collaboration with his brother Josef, titled **Pizzicato Polka.**

VIENNESE COMPOSERS

There are also two fine examples of modern Viennese dance composition in Franz Lehar's **Gold and Silver** and **Merry Widow** waltzes, and another in the set of waltzes from **The Waltz Dream** by Oscar Straus, who, by the way, is in no way related to the famous Strauss family spoken of above.

ITALIAN COMPOSERS

The dance music of Italy is not heard as much over the air as that of other countries, although it is used considerably in concert form—particularly the tarantelle. In this volume, however, we have two examples of fine waltz writing in Ernest Becucci's **My Treasure** and Pestalozza's **Ciribiribin** waltzes, both melodically and rhythmically in keeping with the Italian temperament.

EMIL WALDTEUFEL

Foremost among French dance composers is Emil Waldteufel, a concert dance orchestra leader who attained a pre-eminence in Parisian circles similar to that awarded Johann Strauss, Jr., in Vienna. Waldteufel's waltzes rival those of Strauss as regards popularity—for that reason twelve of them are included in this volume. First we find the brilliant **España,** founded on the themes, Spanish in origin, used also by Emanuel Chabrier in his famous rhapsody; then the touching **Always or Never,** the melancholy **Dolores,** the naïve **Trés Jolie,** the sentimental **My Dream,** then another set of Spanish waltzes, founded on folk themes and titled **Estudiantina.** The gracefully intriguing **Skaters** follows, then the fascinating **Sirens** and then a set, glorifying Nature, titled **Return of Spring;** there is a graceful sway to the exquisite **Angel of Love,** a note of sadness in the **Au Revoir,** and a breath of sweet perfume in **Violets.**

OTHER FRENCH COMPOSERS

But there are many other French dance compositions broadcast, and several of the choicest are to be found in this volume—for example, Auguste Bosc's characteristic **March of the Little Pierrots** and his dainty valse lente titled **Moss Rose;** Maurice Depret's exquisite **April Smiles** waltzes, Louis Ganne's stirring march-twostep **Lorraine,** which was used so much by French Army bands during the World War. You will also find an arrangement of the famous **Apache Dance,** the main theme of which is taken from one of Offenbach's operettas. Another exquisite waltz mosaic often broadcast is Mezzacapo's **Sympathie** and almost every one is familiar with the **Valse Bleue** by Alfred Margis. There is also one lively dance in Borel-Clerc's **La Sorella.**

TANGOS

Spanish, Mexican, and Cuban composers have developed the tango from a musical standpoint into a fancy dance unrivalled in popularity. It is equally in favor with the music lover, so this volume contains a series of splendid tangos in **Spanish Love** by Esteban-Marti, **Gaucho** by Gonzaga, **El Irresistible** by Logatti (a tango popular for a good many years), **Dengozo** by Ernest Nazareth (another firmly established favorite), and **El Choclo** by Villoldo. There is also an exquisite Spanish waltz, **Over the Waves,** by Juventino Rosas.

MISCELLANEOUS NUMBERS

Several dance compositions, frequently heard over the air and written by composers of various nations, are also to be found in this volume, among them Bucalossi's fascinating gipsy waltzes titled **La Gitana,** Corbin's **Santiago,** a waltz in Spanish style, and D'Arcy Jaxone's serenading waltzes, **La Serenata,** with the charming vocal refrain. Another favorite is Fucik's flashing **Entry of the Gladiators** march and two highly colored characteristic waltzes, **Monte Cristo,** by Ivan Kotlar, and **Waves of the Danube,** by Josef Ivanovici.

On The Beautiful Blue Danube

Waltzes

Johann Strauss

Tempo di Valse

1.

p

Ped. ✻ Ped.

✻ Ped. ✻ Ped.

✻ Ped. ✻ Ped. ✻

ff *fz* *fz* *p*

Ped. ✻ Ped. ✻ Ped. ✻ Ped. ✻ Ped. ✻

f

Ped. *simile*

p
f
1.
2.
tr
p
D.S.
Ending.
Fine
2.
3/4
mf
1
f
p
2.
Fine
p dolce
pp
p
D.S. al Fine.
mf

3
p
p cresc.
f
1.
p
2.
p
p
p
fz
1.
p
2.
p
Ending.
D. S.
4.
f
p
p

Ending.
D.S.
5.

D. C. ad lib al 𝄐

Morning Journals

Waltzes

Johann Strauss

1.
2.
p
p
D.C. al Fine
2.
p

p
p
f
1.
2.
p
D.S. al Fine
3.
p
Fine

f
1
2
D. S. al Fine
4.
p
1
Fine
2
f
f

1
2
D. C. al Fine
5.
f
Fine
f
2
p
f
pp
pp
1
sf
p
2
f
D.S. al Fine

Roses From The South

Waltzes

Johann Strauss

1.
mf
2.
f
p
p
fz
2.
p
pp

1.
Fine.
p
tr
2.
f
D. S. al Fine.
3.

p
f
p
1.
2.
4.
marcato.
p
f
8va

8va
ff

Artist Life

Waltzes

1.
2.
Fine
f
p
D.C. al Fine
2.
p
cresc.
pp

cresc.
f
pp
f
2 3 4 1
p
pp
1.
pp
2.
Fine
D.C. al Fine

3.
p
f
1.
Fine.
D.S.
4.
p
f

5.

Treasure Waltz
(Gipsy Baron)

Johann Strauss

D.S. al Fine.
2
1.
2.

f
p
p
p
pp
cresc.
f
f
f
p
f

3
1.
2.

4
mf
f
1.
Fine.
D.S. al Fine.

Tales from the Vienna Woods

Waltzes

Johann Strauss

2.
p
mf
pp
f
cresc.
1.
2.
Fine

3.
p
p
f
pp
1.
2. Fine
p
mf
mf
1.
2.
D.S. al Fine
mf
f
f
p

4.
p
f
1.
2.
p dolce
cresc.
Fine

5.
mf
pp
f
Fine
mf
fz
D. S. al Fine
1.
2.

New Vienna

Waltzes

Johann Strauss

fz
p
poco cresc.
f
1
2.
f
p
2
3/4
f
p
f
p
p
f
p
1
2
Fine

ff
rit.
pp poco rit.
a tempo
p
rit.
pp poco rit.
a tempo
cresc.
1
f
2
pp
f
f
p
D.S. al Fine
3
f
f
p poco rit.
mf a tempo
to Fine
f
1
f
2
f
Fine
fz

f
f
p
f
p
pp
cresc.
D. S. al Fine

4
f
p
f
poco rit.
a tempo
poco rit.
a tempo
1.
2. Fine
ff
ff
1.
2.
f
D.S. al Fine

Wine, Woman and Song

Waltzes

2.
f
pp
pp
ff
pp
pp
f
1
2
Fine
p dolce
f

D.S. al Fine
3.

p
f
f
f
fz
1
2
p
Fine
4.
f
p

f
f
f
1
2
p
f
tr
D.S. al
1
2
p
CODA
3
4
f

Voices of Spring

Waltzes

Johann Strauss

p
tr
f
p
p
tr
f
tr
f
f
mf

p dolce
mf
p dolce
mf
p
f
p dolce

tr
f
f
tr
p dolce
poco ritard.
f
p
f
p

poco ritard.
a tempo
p dolce
mf
tr

p
poco rit.
fz poco rit.
a tempo
poco rit.
fz
a tempo
fz poco rit.

Vienna Blood

Waltzes

Johann Strauss

2.
f
p
p
1
2
cresc.
f
1.
2.
Fine.

3.
f
cresc.
1.
2.
p
ff
pp
fz
Fine.

4.
f
cresc.
1.
2.
p
f
ff
1.
2.
f

One Heart, One Mind

Polka - Mazurka

Johann Strauss

p
mf
f
Trio.
p
fz
f
1.
2.
p
p
f
pp
f
f
D.C. ad lib.

Pizzicato - Polka

Johann and Josef Strauss

ff
p molto stacc.
ff
p
D.C. to Coda.
Più Allegro.
Coda.
ff

España

Waltzes

Emil Waldteufel

Arioso
2
p
1
2
ff
Fine
Risoluto
D C al Fine
Leggiero
3
sf

sf
cresc
f
sf
ff
1.
2.
p
f
Con spirito
sf
sf
sf
sf
Amabile
p
1.
2.
4
f
Energico
f
p
sf
f
p
sf
glissando
sf

glissando
3
sf
sf
1.
2.
Con spirito
ff
p
ff
p
ff
p
ff
ben marcato
ff
1.
2.
Fine

Always or Never

(Toujours ou Jamais)

Emil Waldteufel

Espressivo
2
p
ben marcato
sf
p
1.
2.
mf
con grazia
cresc.
f
1.
2.
Fine

Grandioso
3
ff
mf poco
a
poco
cresc.
ff
1.
2.
con grazia
p
f
con fuoco
ff
1.
2.

semplice
4
mf
ff
con fuoco
1.
2.

Violets

Waltzes

Emil Waldteuful

scherzando
2
p
f
p
f
p
f
cresc.
1.
2.
con fuoco
ff
p
grazioso
p
1.
2.
3.
p
D.S.

con dolcezza
3
p
cresc.
dim.
ff risoluto
1.
2.

con espressione
4
p
legato e
pp
leggiero
cresc.
p
pp
1.
2.

Dolores

Waltzes

Emil Waldteufel

grazioso
2
p
mf
p
mf
p
cresc.
dim.
1
p
2
mf
animato
f
mf

1
2
Fine
mf
p
D.S. al Fine
semplice
3
p
cresc.
dim.
1
2
ff
Fine
con fuoco
ff
1
2
D.S. al Fine

4.
scherzando
mf
cresc.
f
1
2
arioso
p
cresc.
sf
p
1
2
Fine
mf
D.S. al Fine

Tres - Jolie

Waltzes

E. Waldteufel

2.

3.
grazioso
cresc.
f
p
Ped.
cresc.
dim.
p
D. C.

Waltz D.C. ad lib.

My Dream
Waltzes

E. Waldteufel

1.-2.
3.
D.C. al 3
2.
p dolce
cresc.
dim.
1.
2.
p
ff
Fine

1.
2.
3.
p
D.C. al 3
3.
p espressivo
leggiero
cresc.
dim.
1
2
f
con fuoco

ff marcato
f
D.C. al 3
4.
p grazioso
cresc.
rit.
a tempo
ff
p
pp
mezzo voce

cresc.
dim.
1.
Fine
D. C. al Fine

Estudiantina.
Waltzes.

Emile Waldteufel.

3
ff
p
1
f
2

2.
p espressivo.
Fine.
ff
p
ff
p
ff
D.S.

3.
1.
2.
Fine.

1.
2.
f
D.S.
4.
p
mf
1.
2.
Fine.
ff ben marcato.
1.
2.
D.S.

The Skaters
Waltzes

E. Waldteufel

p
cresc.
p
1.
2.
p
Fine.

risoluto.
2.

3.
p espressivo.
cresc. poco a poco.
Più cresc.
3
p
1.
2.
p
grazioso.
f
p
f
1.
p
2.

4.
mf amabile
cresc.
sf
1.
Fine.
2.
mf leggiero
D. C. ad lib al Fine.
f
mf
f
mf
f
mf
f
mf
1.
mf
2.
D.C. al Fine.

The Sirens

Waltzes

p
p
2.
con fuoco
ff
1.
2.

con espressione
p
cresc.
dim.
f grandioso
3.
scherzando
p
8va
poco a poco cresc.
f
1.
2.
p
f

Più mosso
p
ff
f
1.
2.
grandioso
mf
4.

p
f
p
Fine
scherzando
f
1.
2.
D. C.
al Fine

Angel of Love

Waltzes

Emile Waldteufel

2.
passionato
sf
sf.
dim.
p
mf
p ben legato
cresc.
dim.

3.
energico
ff
ff
ff
1.
2.
ff
mf scherzando
1.
2.
f

4.
f passionato
p
f
p
1
2
f ben marcato
p
1
2

Return of Spring

Waltzes

Emil Waldteufel

1.
2.
p
rit.
a tempo
mf
f
p

Leggiero
2
p
f
1.
2.
Espressivo
p
f
p
cresc.
f
dim.
p
cresc.
f
dim.

Con spirito
3
p
f
1.
2.
Passionato
f
f
ff
p
1.
2.

4
p
cresc.
f
1.
p
2.
p dolce
dolce
cresc.
sf
a tempo
p rit.
cresc.
f
1.
p
2.

Au Revoir

Waltzes

Emile Waldteufel

ff
marcato
p
ff
p
poco a poco cresc.
p leggiero
1
ff
2
ff
Con tenerezza
2.
p
cresc.
f
f
f
dim.
1
p
2
p

Scherzando
3
3
3
3
3
3
f
1.
2.
p
Risoluto
3.
f
con fuoco
1.
2.
p
Con espressione

1.
2.
4.
ben legato
p
cresc.
dim.
1.
2.
p
ff
Con fuoco
3
1.
2.
Fine
8va
8va
8va
p
D.S.

5.
Amabile
p
1.
2.
Scherzando
cresc.
f
dim.
1.
p
2.

The Doll

Waltzes

Jos. Bayer

p
mf
f
1.
2.
D. C. al Fine.
2.
f
mf

Fine.
mf
mf
D. S. al Fine.

3.
pp
Fine.
ff
D.C. al Fine

La Gitana

Waltzes

E. Bucalossi

mf
ff
1.
mf
cresc.
sf
Ped.
2.
mf
sf
pesante D.C. al Fine
2.
mf
scherzando
cresc.
sf
1
2.
sf

ff
p
f
cresc.
ff
Ped.
p
1.
Last.
mf
D.S.
Fine.
3.
p
p

sf
p
sf
sf
p
f
p
sf
p
sf
p
cresc.
3
sf
f

ff
1.
Last.
D. S.
Fine.
Legato e con espress.
4.
p

cresc.
1.
2.
sf
ff
mf
Ped.
*
Fine.

Ciribiribin

Waltz

A. Pestalozza

poco rit.
a tempo.
mf
f
poco a poco.
rall.
a tempo.

p
f
f
p
p
rall.
a tempo.
ff

ff
poco rit.
sfff

Flirtation

Waltzes

P. A. Steck

tr
mf
pp
mf
pp

a tempo.
rit.
mf
pp
mf
pp
cresc.
un poco rall.
a tempo.
pp

a tempo.
poco rall.
marcato
pp
p subito
p
pp
morendo

Gold And Silver

Waltzes

F. Lehar

p
f
1.
2.
pp
2.
mf
p
1.
2.
p

scherzando
1.
2.
3.
f
mf
p
f
p

p
mf
f
1.
2.

Gondolier

1.
2.
mf
cresc.
f

2.
f

3.
p
1.
2.
Fine
1.
2.
D.C. al Fine

Jolly Fellows
Waltzes

R. Vollstedt

Tempo di Valse

1.

p

con Ped.

sf

sf

sf

sf

1.

2. *Fine.*

f

sf

f
fz
sfz
D. C. al Fine.
2.
3/4
p
sfz

142
a tempo
mf
1.
2.
Con passione
1.
2.

3.
con passione
fz
1.
2.
rit.
a tempo
mf
ff
de - - -
cresc.

Love's Dreamland

Waltzes

Otto Roeder

f
1.
2.
D. C. al Fine.
2.
3
4
mp
f
mp

f
1.
2.
ff
1.
2.
3.
p

espress.
mf
cresc.
f
1.
2.
mf
cresc.
f
1.
2.
D.C. ad lib.

Monte Cristo

Hungarian-Waltz

I. Kotlar

sf
p
più f
sf
poco più a capriccio.
mf

150
a tempo.
string e cresc.
dim. e rall.
animando
string e cresc.
dim. e rall.
a tempo.
f con fuoco.
meno.
p e dim.
molto rall.

Piu lento.
p
f
f
Piu lento.
lento.
Presto.
legg.
pp
ppp
8va

Over The Waves

Waltzes

Energico
ff
Energico
ff
p
1.
2.
2.
ff
mf

8va
ff
8va
1.
2.
ff
ff
p

ff
p
1
2
ff
p
f

Santiago

Spanish Waltzes.

A. Corbin

3
mf
8va
8va

8va
cresc.
f
8va
ff
3
3
8va
Fine
amoroso
f
p

f
ff
D.C. ad lib.

Sourire d'Avril

(April-Smiles)

ff
1.
2.
p
D.C. al Fine.
Cantabile.
2.
f
pp
1.

2.
Fine.
leggiero
p
cresc.
dim.
D.C. al Fine
3.
p
f
1.
pp

2.
p
espress.
p
f
1.
pp
2.

Vienna Beauties

Waltzes

C. M. Ziehrer

p
f
p
D. C. al Fine.
2.
f
p

f
f
p
f
fp
fp
1.
2.
ff
3.
f
rit.
p
a tempo.

f
p
f
p
1.
2.

Waves Of The Danube

Waltzes

J. Ivanovici

2.
p
1.
2.
rit.
p
1.
2.
Last.
rit.
D.S.

3.
mf
p
dolce
1.
2.
p
p
f
1.
2.
Last.
p
p
D.S.

4.
mf
1.
2.
Last.
Fine.
f
tr
ff
p
D.S. al Fine.

Sympathie

Waltzes

E. Mezzacapo

a tempo.
fff
ff
p dolce.
f rit.
a tempo.
ff
ff
p
rit.
D. C. al Fine.
2.
ff
pp

ff
pp
ff
dolce
leggiero
1.
2.
rall.
rit.
a tempo.
mf

cresc.
f
p
3.
mf
p avec élégance
f
p poco rall.
a tempo

cresc.
f
p
cresc.
D.C. ad lib. al Fine.

La Serenata

Italian Waltzes

Tempo di Valse

D'Arcy Jaxone

2.
ing
light.
The
night! Good
night! Good
night!
And
dream
of
me
till
morn -
ing
light.
f
1.
2.

2.
f
p
tr
1.
2.
Fine.
mf
f
mf
f
1.
2.
D. S. al Fine.

dolce cantabile.
3.
p
sfz

D. C. al Fine.

My Treasure

Waltzes

E. Becucci

f
p
ff
p espress
pp
f
p
cresc.
f
p
1.
Fine

2.
p
pp stacc.
p
pp stacc.
f
p
p
p

cresc.
f
marcato.
pp
p
pp stacc.
p
pp stacc.
f
p
p

3.
p
con Ped.
p scherzando
cresc.
1
2
ff con fuoco
p
ff
1.
2.
p

The Merry Widow

Waltzes

Con brio
ff
p
mf-p
sf
sff
Grazioso con espressione
2.
mp

ff
p
mf
sf
sf
f
mf
mf

ff
sf
3.
mf
f
mf
sf
sf

sf
f
1.
2.

A Waltz Dream

Waltzes

Oscar Straus

a tempo
pp
p
mf
p
mf
cresc.
f
cresc.
ff
f

2.
mf
fz
fz
fz
p
p
cresc.
f
mf

cresc.
p
f
fz
ff
8va
fz
3.
f

ff
rit.
p cantabile
mp
cresc.
f
mf
ff
f

ff
ff
4.
mf
f
mf

f
fz
fz
fz
cresc.
f
fz
ff

Haven Of Happiness

Valse Lente

J. T. Steger

f e suelto
marc.
sf
p e scherz.
f
pp
con grazia
1
2
p
p elegando
cantando
f e suelto

sf
scherz.
tr
p
molto express.
pp una corda
poco f
expansivo
f
p
sf
pp

p
sf
f p e con grazia
f e con brio
ff
p
f marc
ff
p delicado
pp rall
a tempo elegante

sf
anim. e cresc.
f
p rall
a tempo elegante
f muy suelto
f
tr
p
tr
pp
dolce sordina
ppp
tr
ff risoluto
fff

Moss Rose
(Entr'acte)

A. Bosc

f
simili
mf
a tempo
f
mf
rit.
molto rit.
1.
2.
p poco rall.
D.S. al Fine
TRIO
ff
p
ritard.
p
ben cantanto
simili
cresc.
dim.

p
cresc.
dim. et ritard
p
Più Vivo.
mf
Ped.
simili
ff
a tempo
Ped.
Ped.
simili

ritard.
p et rall.
a tempo
Ped.
simili
rall.
a tempo
p
Più lento
p
pp
Più vivo
Ped.
p

Sounds from Home
Landler-Waltzes

No. 2
p
tr
Ped.
simile
fp
tr
p
tr
tr
tr
tr
tr
p
tr
fp
tr

No. 3
p
Ped.
simile
f
p

No. 4
p
Ped.
simile
pp

Valse Bleue

Alfred Margis

f
Ped. * Ped. * Ped. * Ped. simile
p
f
Ped. * Ped. * Ped. simile
D.S. 𝄋 al Fine.
TRIO
ben cantando
mf
Ped. * Ped. * Ped. * Ped. * Ped. * simile

cresc.
mf
Ped.
simile
marcato il canto
mf
p dolce
mf marc.

p dolce
Tempo I
dolce
mf
Ped.
simile.
rit.
a tempo

Sunshine and Shadow

Valse Lente

Ch. Henrique

energique
rall.
rall.
TRIO Valse boston
f
f

mf
Sentimental
f
mf
energique
rall.
ff
ff
ff
fff
Sec
8

Night Frolic

Valse Lente

W. Spacek

f
1.
2.
D.S. 𝄋 al Fine
f
p
Trio
mf
m.g.
f
p

p
p
ff
sfz
sfz
1.
2.
D.S. 𝄋 al Fine

Apache Dance

Valse Lente

Arr. by A. Hewitt.

pressez
Vivo
ff
a tempo
p
cresc.
Vivo.
ff
p rall. e dim.
Tempo I.
p
sfz
sf
sf
p a tempo
poco accel.
cresc.
rit. sff
sf a tempo

Mazurka ben marcato
ff energico.
p
Valse Vivo.
ff
Valse
ff
ff
sf
sffz

Entry Of The Gladiators

March

Julius Fucîk

ff
Octava ad lib
ff
1.
2.
Trio.
f
mf
p
sf
fz
marc.

dim.
mf
cresc.
Grandioso.
rit.
fff
a tempo.
sf
8va
8va
rit.
a tempo.
8va
più mosso.
sf

March Of The Little Pierrots.

Auguste Bosc

f
ff
1
2
f
ff
Fine.

Trio.
mp
cresc.
mf
D.C. al Fine.

La Sorella

Two-Step

Ch. Borel-Clerc

mf
sfz
sf
f
ff
to Coda.
f

p
Trio.
p Cantando
f
ff
p
ff
f
D. S.
Coda.
ff

Skirt Dance
"FAUST UP TO DATE"
Schottische

Meyer Lutz

1st time p 2nd time f
Fine
D.S. al Fine

Lorraine
Two-Step

Louis Ganne

fz
f
sf
f
sf
mf
sf
1.
2.
dim.
legg e grazioso.
ff
ff
ff
f
ff
Fine.

Trio.
p dolce e molto cantabile.
p
f
p
f
ff sonoriss.
p
cresc.
f
ff

p
cresc.
f
ff
Con forza.
fff altieramente.
fff
1.
2.
f
D.C. al Fine

Dengozo

(Tango)

Ernest Nazareth

leggiero
p
1.
2.

ritard.
sf
Staccato
p
sfz
mf
p
sfz
p

1.
2.
p
mf
senza ritard
sfz
sfz

Gaúcho

Tango

Fr. Gonzaga

Tranquillo
mp
mp
f
mp
D. C. al Fine
f

El Irresistible

Argentine Tango

L.Logatti

p
fz
fz
fz
fz
marcato
rit.
a tempo
p
fz
fz
fz

p
f
f
Fine

TRIO
p
ff
D. C. al Fine

Spanish Love

(Tango)

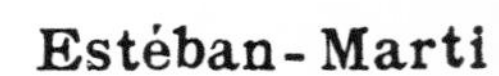

legato
p
mf
p
f
p
pp dolce
mf
pp
p

f
rit.
Tempo I.
p
mf

cresc.
rit.
a tempo
5
cresc.
p
più tranquillo
pp
dolciss
8

El Choclo

Tango

A. G. Villoldo

ff
p
cresc.
f
ff
mf
cresc.
f

dolce
p
f
dim.
mf
f